We're in this Together

Peter Leigh

Published in association with
The Basic Skills Agency

Hodder & Stoughton

A MEMBER OF THE HODDER HEADLINE GROUP

Acknowledgements
Cover: Matthew Williams
Illustrations: Josephine Blake

Orders: please contact Bookpoint Ltd, 130 Milton Park, Abingdon, Oxon OX14 4SB. Telephone: (44) 01235 827720, Fax: (44) 01235 400454. Lines are open from 9.00 - 6.00, Monday to Saturday, with a 24 hour message answering service. Email address: orders@bookpoint.co.uk

British Library Cataloguing in Publication Data
A catalogue record for this book is available from The British Library

ISBN 0 340 84900 2

First published 2002

Impression number	10 9 8 7 6 5 4 3 2 1
Year	2007 2006 2005 2004 2003 2002

Typeset by SX Composing DTP, Rayleigh, Essex.
Printed in Great Britain for Hodder & Stoughton Educational, a division of Hodder Headline Plc, 338 Euston Road, London NW1 3BH by Athenaeum Press, Gateshead, Tyne & Wear.

About the Play

The People

- **Jethro**
- **David**

The Place

Outside the Headteacher's office.

What's happening

Jethro *and* **David** *are sat outside the Headteacher's office.*

***Jethro** and **David** are sat outside the*
Headteacher's office.
There is a long silence.
*Finally **Jethro** speaks.*

Jethro Do you think we're really
in it this time?

Silence

Well, they can't blame it on me . . .

Another silence.

I said they can't . . .

David I heard what you said.

Jethro Well it's true . . .
It wasn't my fault, was it?
So they can't blame it on me,
can they. . .?
Can they?

David Yes they can.
And they will.

Jethro No, they can't.
What do you mean?
It wasn't my fault.

David Jethro, it was your fault.
Totally your fault.
One hundred per cent your fault.
And they will blame it on you.
All on you.
And they will be right.
There's only one thing wrong
about this, and that's me
sitting here next to you.
Because I didn't do anything,
but I'm in trouble because of you.
Not for the first time, I might add.

Jethro Oh yes? Did I hear right?
'I didn't do anything?'
Is that what you said?
Because if anyone's
to blame for this,
then that person is sitting
not a million miles from me.

David What? Me?
It's my fault, is it?
Yes, of course. You're right!
Naughty, naughty me!
Bad boy, David!
I don't think so Jethro,
I don't think so at all!

Jethro Well, who was it
who set the fire alarm off?

David Yes, it was me. I know.
And why did I set it off?
Because the school was on fire.
That's why.
Hundreds of kids were going
to burn to death . . .

Jethro Oh, come on.
Don't exaggerate.

David Don't exaggerate?
Don't exaggerate??
What about the roaring flames?
What about the belching smoke?

Jethro There wasn't any belching smoke
or roaring flames.
There were two towels, that's all.
They were a bit scorched.
Nothing more.

David Thanks to me and the fire alarm.

Jethro It's not thanks to you at all.
You didn't need
to set the alarm off.

David It's better to be safe than sorry.

Jethro And you didn't need
to go running round the school
screaming 'Fire! Fire!'
at the top of your voice.
And you didn't need
to spray foam everywhere.

David Well, as I say. Better safe than sorry.
But the real point is,
the point you're missing in all this,
is who set light to those towels
in the first place?
Answer me that.

Jethro Well – that wasn't my fault.

David How can you say that?
The fire started in
the changing rooms.
Behind one of the radiators.
You were in the changing rooms.
You threw a lighted cigarette
behind the radiator.
That means it's your fault.
Yours, and no-one else's.

Jethro Well, all right.
Yes there was a fire,
and yes, I suppose I did start it.

David 'Suppose?'
How can you 'suppose' you
lit a fire?
You either did or you didn't.

Jethro Well, I admit it.
I did light the fire.
But I didn't mean to.

David Oh that's a great excuse –
I didn't mean to.
Whoever started those fires in
Australia didn't mean to.
Whoever sunk the Titanic
didn't mean to.
But they still happened.

Jethro Look, in the first place,
that cigarette,
it wasn't mine.
I don't smoke. You know that.

David Then whose was it?

Jethro It was Ashley's.

David Ashley?
The big kid in year 11?

Jethro That's right.
He was having a fag
in the changing rooms,
when he saw this teacher coming.
So he gave it to me,
so he wouldn't get into trouble.
Then he walked off.

David He gave it to you?
Just like that?
And you took it?

Jethro Listen, you don't say no
to Ashley.

David Well, why didn't you stub it out?

Jethro I didn't like to.
I thought he'd come back
in a minute.
But then the teacher
kept coming closer.

So I threw it away,
just to get rid of it.

David And where did you throw it?

Jethro Behind the radiator.

David Exactly.

Jethro Well I didn't know
there'd be any old towels there.

David There are always old towels
behind radiators
in changing rooms.
Or socks. Or sweet papers.
Or drink cartons.
You look behind any radiator
and you will see old socks
or old towels or old rubbish.
Everyone knows that.
And because it is nice and warm
there, it's also very dry.
So what do you do? –
being the sensible,
intelligent boy you are –
you throw a lighted cigarette
in the middle of it,
that's what you do.
And then stupid me, of course,
in the wrong place at the wrong
time, as ever, I come along.
And when I see the flames
and the smoke . . .

Jethro There weren't any flames
or smoke.
You're exaggerating again.
There was one tiny little wisp.
That was all.

David Well there would have been
if I hadn't got it with
the extinguisher
and set the fire alarm off.
As a result of which
I am sat here with you.
Outside the head's office,
in the worst trouble of my life.
I'm probably going to be expelled,
my mum is going to kill me
when I get home.
And all because of you.

Jethro Oh yes, well you're not so
blameless, are you?

David What do you mean?

Jethro You've got a few questions to
answer.

David What questions?

Jethro Like, what were you
doing there in the first place?

David What do you mean?

Jethro Why were you in the boys'
changing rooms?

David What's that got to do with it?
That's got nothing to do with it.
I was there. That's all.
And it was very lucky I was.

Jethro Yes, but you shouldn't
have been there, should you?
You should've been in French.
But you were hiding
in the boys' changing room,
weren't you?

David No I wasn't.

Jethro Yes you were.
And what's more, I know
why you were hiding there.

David Why?

Jethro It's that girl, isn't it?

David What girl?

Jethro You know – Beccy.
The one you've been chatting up
for the last month.

David I haven't been chatting her up.

Jethro Yes you have.
I've seen you –
always hanging round her and
smiling at her –
Beccy this and Beccy that.
Waiting outside her classroom
door, so you can just
happen to bump into her.

David I haven't!

Jethro Yes you have.
And that's what you were doing –
waiting to meet her
as she came out of the girls'
changing rooms.

David Well, so what if I was.

Jethro Well, you met her all right,
didn't you?
You really met her.
You met her with a full-on
spray of fire extinguisher.

David It was an accident.
She just happened to be
in the way.

Jethro Oh she's really going to believe
that, isn't she . . .
With her nice new skirt ruined,
having to be sent home
to get changed . . .
She's really going to believe
it was an accident.

David Well it was.

Jethro It doesn't matter
if it was or it wasn't.
She's not going to believe it,
is she?

David I know, I know.
She'll not look at me now.
And it was going so well.
We were really getting on.
And now it's finished.
You ruined it.

Jethro Me?
What's it got to do with me?
I had nothing to do with it.
I didn't point the nozzle at her.

David I didn't point it at her.
It twisted in my hand,
and she just happened to be near –
that's all.
But the point is,
I wouldn't even be holding it
if it wasn't for you.
Honestly Jethro,
it's always the same.
As soon as I see a nice girl,
and am getting on
really well with her,
you step in and spoil it.

Jethro Me? I don't.

David Yes you do.
Remember Kayleigh Bayley
at our old school?

Jethro What about her?

David It was going really well with her.
We were spending
all dinnertime together,
and walking home together –
she even let me hold her hand once.
Until you told her
I used to eat frogs.

Jethro Well, you did keep tadpoles.

David There is a difference
between keeping a jar of tadpoles
and having them on toast for
breakfast.

Jethro It was just a joke.

David Yes, but she didn't think so.
Especially after you put one
in her lunchbox.
It jumped right out at her.
She screamed for ten minutes.
Her mum had to come in
and collect her.
And I got the blame for that too.

Jethro But you've got to admit,
it was a laugh.

David For you maybe, but not for me.
And what about Kylie Smiley?

Jethro Kylie Smiley?
The one with the —?

David Yes, that one.
It was even better with her.
I'd been round to tea at her house,
her dad used to take me
to football matches,
everything was going great –
until you stepped in.

Jethro What did I do?

David You know very well
what you did.
You said I was taking
three different girls to a party.

Jethro Well you were.

David Yes, but they were aged
four, five, and six.
And it was their cousin's
birthday party.
All jellies and ice cream.

Jethro Well you could have
explained that.

David I didn't get the chance.
She never spoke to me again.

Jethro Well, you were better off
without her.
She'd have had you married
as soon as you were old enough.

David I can decide that for myself,
thank you very much.
I don't need you butting in.

Jethro Just lending a helping hand,
that's all.

David Well, I can do without your help.
It's your help
that's got me into trouble before.

Jethro Like when, for example?

David Like when I was carrying that paint
up the stairs to the art room.
I was doing fine,
until you decided to help.
And then I spent two hours after
school cleaning the stairs.

Jethro That was an accident.

David Accident? Is that what you call it?
And what about that time
in the dinner hall?
With the custard?
That was you helping again,
but it was me who had to pay
for the special cleaning
of Miss's dress.

Jethro I had to pay too.
And I had to clean the stairs as well.

David Yes, but you did it.
It's always the same with you,
Jethro, ever since Junior School –
you do something and
I get the blame.

Jethro That's because we're mates –
all for one, and one for all,
share and share alike.

David Oh, mates?
Is that what we are?
Well not any more, Jethro.
I'm not the taking the blame
any more for what you've done.
Especially not this time.
You've really done it now.
Whatever you did in the past
is nothing to this.
This is the big one.

Jethro You think so?
You think we're really in it?

David Not me, Jethro, you!

Jethro You're not going to desert me
now, are you?
I thought we were
in this together.
Fine friend you turned out to be.

David It's not a question of friendship.
I'm just going to tell the truth,
that's all.
I'm not taking the blame
for something I didn't do.

Jethro Well I'm not taking the blame
for the fire alarm
and the extinguisher –
you did that.

David Well, I'm not taking
the blame for it.

Jethro And nor am I.

Jethro *and David sit looking away from each other.*

An angry silence.

Finally **Jethro** *says . . .*

Jethro Do you know what this
reminds me of?

Silence

I said do you know –

David No, I don't know what this
reminds you of,
and I don't want to know.

Jethro Go on.
Guess what this reminds me of.

David It reminds you of
Christmas pudding.

Jethro No it doesn't.

David It reminds you of snogging
Britney Spears.

Jethro What?

David It reminds you of fighting aliens
on the planet Zog.

Jethro Don't be silly.
I've never done that.
What does this remind me of?

David I don't know what this
reminds you of.
I don't care what this
reminds you of.
It's bound to be something stupid.

Jethro It reminds me of that film.

David *(despite himself)* What film?

Jethro You know.

David No I don't.

Jethro Yes, you know the one –
where he comes
back from the future
and has to kill his mother,
before he's born, so that he can't . . .
No that's not right . . .
It's his father, that's it.
He has to stop his father
meeting his mother,
something like that.
You know the one I mean.
He keeps saying 'Hasta la vista.'

David Yes I know the one you mean
though I would never have
guessed it.
How does that remind you of this?

Jethro Well you know that bit
where he's waiting for that train.
And if the train goes past,
it's going to crash,
and everyone will be killed.
And he can only stop it
by waving these red knickers
in the air.
And he's standing there for ages,
waving and waving, and the
train gets closer and closer . . .

David That's not the same film.

Jethro Yes it is.

David No it's not.
It's nothing like that film.
There are no two films
more different.

Jethro Well, anyway.

This reminds me of that.

David How can this remind you of that?
How can sitting outside
the Head's office
remind you of waiting for a train?

Jethro Well, you're waiting for it to come,
and you know it's going to be bad,
but you can't get out of it.
You just have to carry on waiting.

David Jethro. Just let me remind you.
For you it may be bad.
In fact, let's not pretend –
it will be bad.
For me – not bad.
I had nothing to do with it.

Jethro Oh come on.
We're in this together.

David No we are not in this together.
We are not in this together at all.
I've spent my life
being in things together with you,
and look where it's got me . . .

The argument is just starting again when the door to the Headteacher's office opens.
Jethro *and* **David** *go quiet.*
A stern voice calls out 'Come in, you two!'
They look at one another, gulp, get up, and slowly walk in.
The door closes behind them.
There is a long silence.
Finally, the door opens again, and **David** *and* **Jethro** *come out.*
As they walk away, they begin to grin.

Jethro The whole school is grateful to us . . .

David We showed quick thinking and common sense . . .

Jethro Ashley owned up to smoking . . .

David And Beccy understood about the skirt . . .

Jethro And she thought it was very brave of us . . .

David (*stops*)
Wait a minute! Wait a minute!
She said 'me', not 'us.'
It was very brave of *me*.

Jethro No, it was 'us.'
Remember, we're in this together.

David No, we are not in this together.
How many times do I
have to tell you . . .

They go off arguing